CONTENTS

Pedigree® Published by Pedigree Books Limited
The Old Rectory, Matford Lane, Exeter, EX2 4PS

£6.99

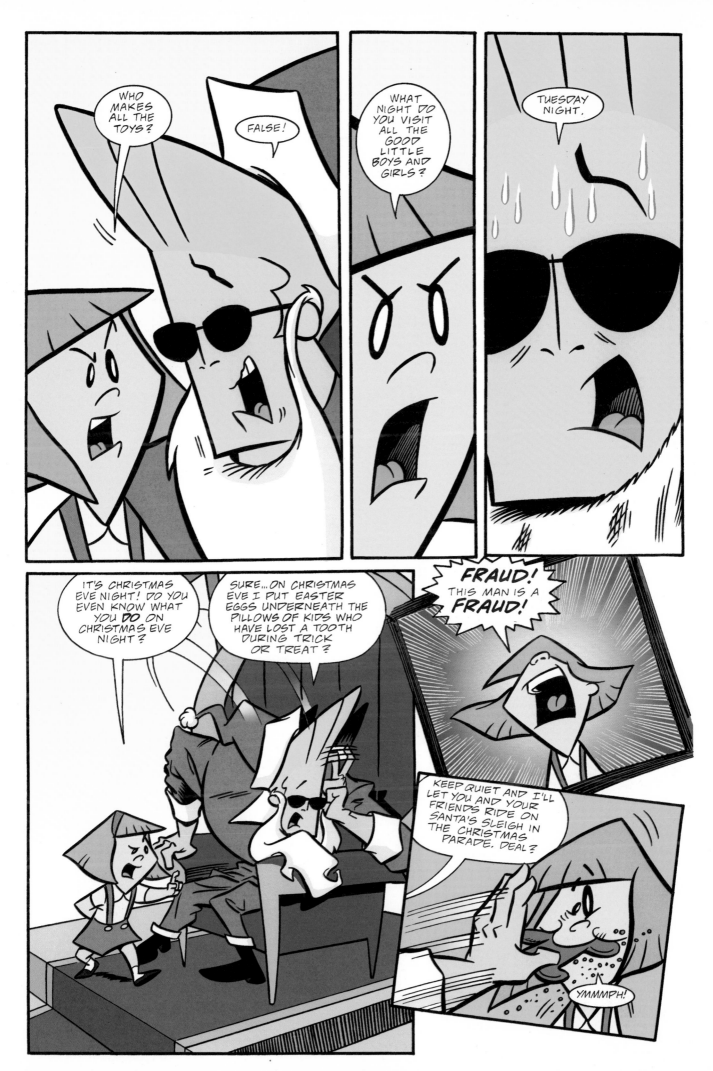

COW and CHICKEN ™

TV or not TV?
(That is the question)

Cow and Chicken are cartoon crazy, spending all their time watching Cartoon Network (unless Mum and Dad turn the TV off because it is bad for their eyes!).

Are you a cartoon buff too? Check out your CNQ - Cartoon Network Quotient - by answering these fun quiz questions ...

1. Complete this famous catchphrase from The Magic Roundabout:
"Time for —-," said Zebedee.
a) Tea b) Bed c) A bath

2. What was eaten by Ned's Newt that made him grow huge?
a) Zippo Newt Food b) Spinach c) Ned

3. Yogi Bear's best friend is called Boo-Hoo.
a) True? b) False?

4. Where do The Flintstones live?
What is the name of their baby?
What is Barney's surname?

5. Which letter of the alphabet completes this cartoon title?
Dragonball
a) X b) Y c) Z

Answers
1 b) Bed
2 a) Zippo Newt Food
3 b) False (It's Boo-Boo, of course)
4 Bedrock
   Pebbles
   Rubble
5 c) Z
6 c) Og
7 Dick Dastardly
8 b) Pigeon
9 a) Officer Dibble
10 b) False

6. Who is missing from this list:
Mike, Lu and ... ?
a) Dougal b) Wilma c) Og

7. Unscramble these letters to find a
well-known Wacky Races character:
CKID STRDYLAAD

8. Complete this world-famous
catchphrase from Wacky Races:
"Stop the ..."
a) Duck b) Pigeon c) Runaway train

9. What is the name of the policeman
in Top Cat?
a) Officer Dibble b) Officer Dribble c)
   PC Copper

10. In its planning stages, Scooby Do
was about a dog who kept getting into
trouble and was called Scooby Don't.
a) True? b) False?

Now try your hand at
being a cartoonist.
Draw Cow and Chicken
- or any other of your
favourite Cartoon
Network characters
- on these blank
television screens

19

WAIT A MINUTE

John Rozum:writer--Mike Stern:pencils--Jeff Albrecht:inks
Ken Bruzenak:letters--Lee Louqhridqe:colors
Harvey Richards:assistant editor--Heidi MacDonald:editor
Dexter's Lab created by Genndy Tartakousky

Day 1...

GOOD, I AM DONE WITH MY HOMEWORK, NOW I CAN GO TO MY LABORATORY AND WORK ON MY...

DEXTER! BEDTIME!

OHHH.

Day 2...

MY CHORES ARE FINISHED! NOW I CAN GO WORK ON MY EXPERIMENT.

DEXTER! GO WASH UP FOR BED!

24

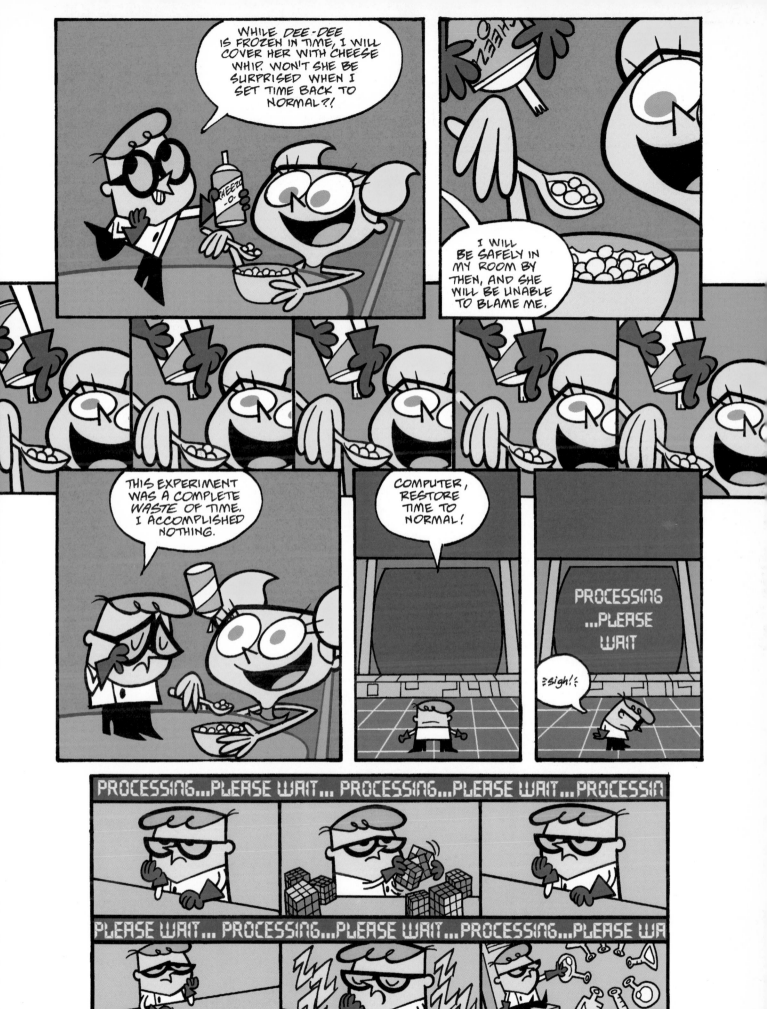

29

DEXTER'S LABORATORY ™

Find the Formula!

Dee-Dee has done it this time! She has annoyed her brother Dexter so much that he has locked himself in his laboratory to work on a special formula. But what is it?

Find out by solving this puzzle. Study the four clues and write your answers into the grid, using the letters already in place to help you. When you have finished, each letter in the grid will have a number-and-letter reference. Use these references to unravel the code at the end.

	A	B	C	D	E
1		H			
2				M	
3			A		
4					G

1   The edge of the sea

2   How to get up a tree or wall

3   Fearless; not a coward

4   Not right!

D3	C3	D4	C2	A1	B1	C2	D4	E4

A2	D1	E1	C3	D2

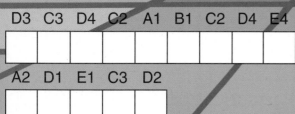

Answer
Dexter has made Dee-Dee some vanishing cream

30

UDDER PERFECTION

DAN SLOTT-writer
TIM HARKINS-artist & letterer
DAVE TANGUAY-colors
HARVEY RICHARDS-assist
HEIDI MACDONALD-edits

COW and CHICKEN
created by
DAVID FEISS

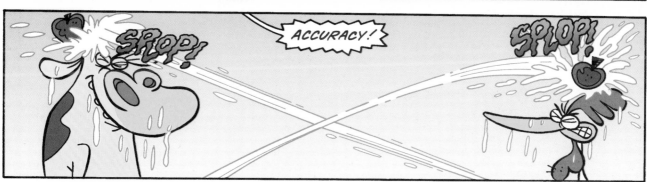

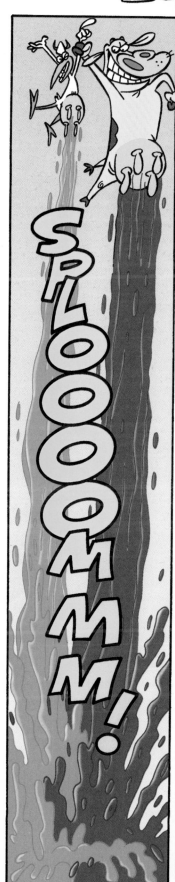

38

COW and CHICKEN ™

Look, everybody. Here are lots of pretty pictures of me an' my big brother, Chicken. Can you spot the two pictures of me that are exactly alike, and then the two pictures of him? Oh, man! This puzzle ain't working' like it should. One of them pictures doesn't show us. Can you point to the imposter? An' who is that guy?

What a pair!

Answers
Matching pairs - pictures 3 and 9 of Cow, pictures 2 and 12 of Chicken
Picture 6 is the odd one out. It shows The Red Guy

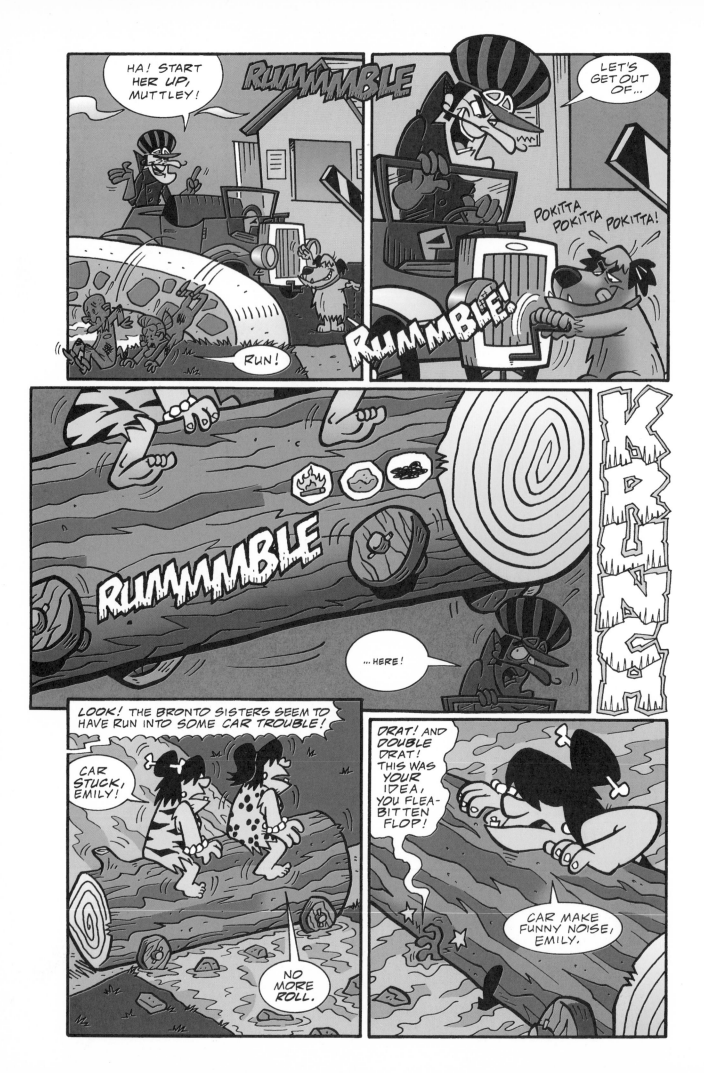

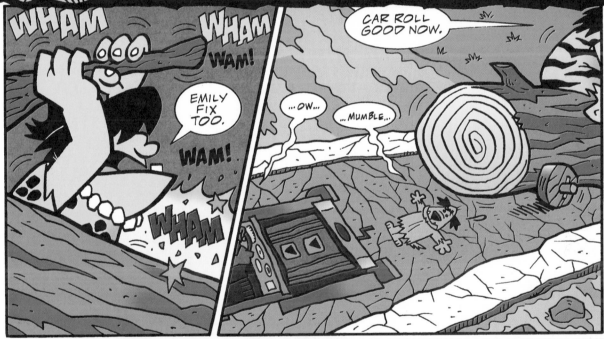

49

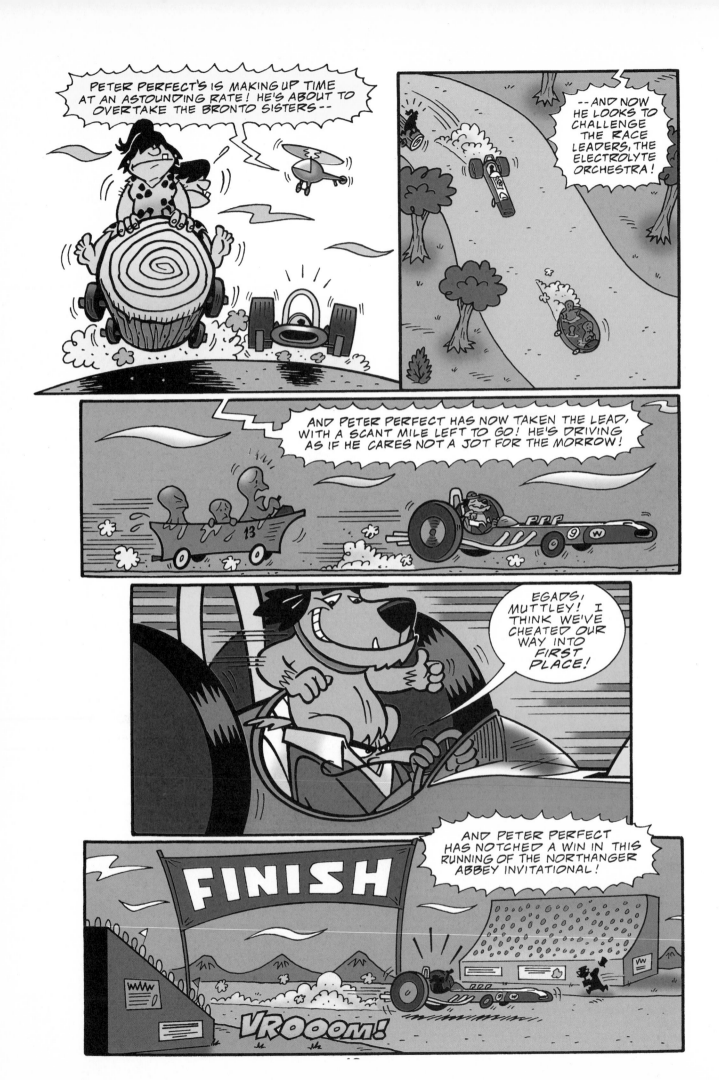

THE END!

There's something wrong here!

Picture the scene - a warm summer's day, a peaceful park and two old friends playing happily together. Well, that's not what we have here!!

There's a furious chase going on round and round the park. Look at the things in the background – they're even wilder! Can you spot Ten Crazy Mistakes? Once you have found them all, use your pencils to colour the picture.

SCOOBY-DOO -IN- THE BEST LAID PLANS...

STORY: CHRIS DUFFY   ART and LETTERING: TIM HARKINS
COLORING: PATRICIA MULVIHILL   EDITING: BRONWYN TAGGART

LATER AT THE HOTEL...

Using the small pictures to guide you, colour these pictures of Blossom, Buttercup and Bubbles –

63

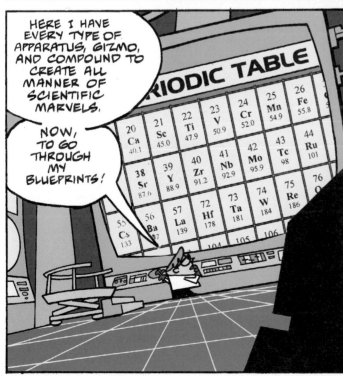

SOMEHOW I MUST GET THEIR ATTENTION.

MY BUBBLE IS SO BIG THEY CANNOT SEE ME!

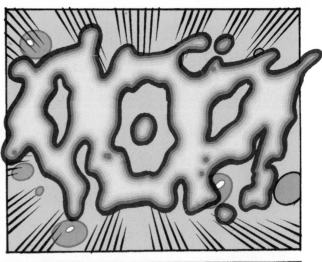

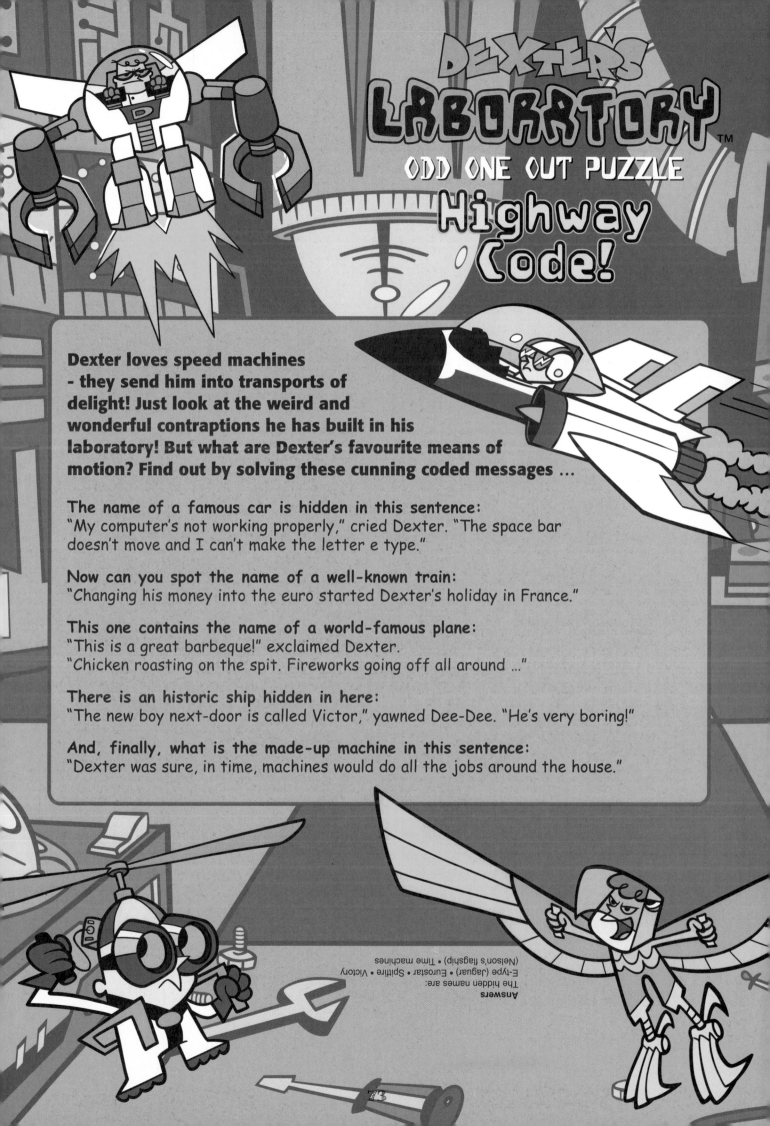

DEXTER'S LABORATORY™
ODD ONE OUT PUZZLE
Highway Code!

Dexter loves speed machines
- they send him into transports of
delight! Just look at the weird and
wonderful contraptions he has built in his
laboratory! But what are Dexter's favourite means of
motion? Find out by solving these cunning coded messages ...

The name of a famous car is hidden in this sentence:
"My computer's not working properly," cried Dexter. "The space bar
doesn't move and I can't make the letter e type."

Now can you spot the name of a well-known train:
"Changing his money into the euro started Dexter's holiday in France."

This one contains the name of a world-famous plane:
"This is a great barbeque!" exclaimed Dexter.
"Chicken roasting on the spit. Fireworks going off all around ..."

There is an historic ship hidden in here:
"The new boy next-door is called Victor," yawned Dee-Dee. "He's very boring!"

And, finally, what is the made-up machine in this sentence:
"Dexter was sure, in time, machines would do all the jobs around the house."

Answers
The hidden names are:
E-type (Jaguar) • Eurostar • Spitfire • Victory
(Nelson's flagship) • Time machines

"BABY-SITTING THE BOVINE"

WRITER: JOE EDKIN
ART: NEAL STERNECKY
LETTERS: PHIL FELIX
COLOR: DAVE TANGUAY
ASSISTS: HARVEY RICHARDS
EDITS: HEIDI MACDONALD

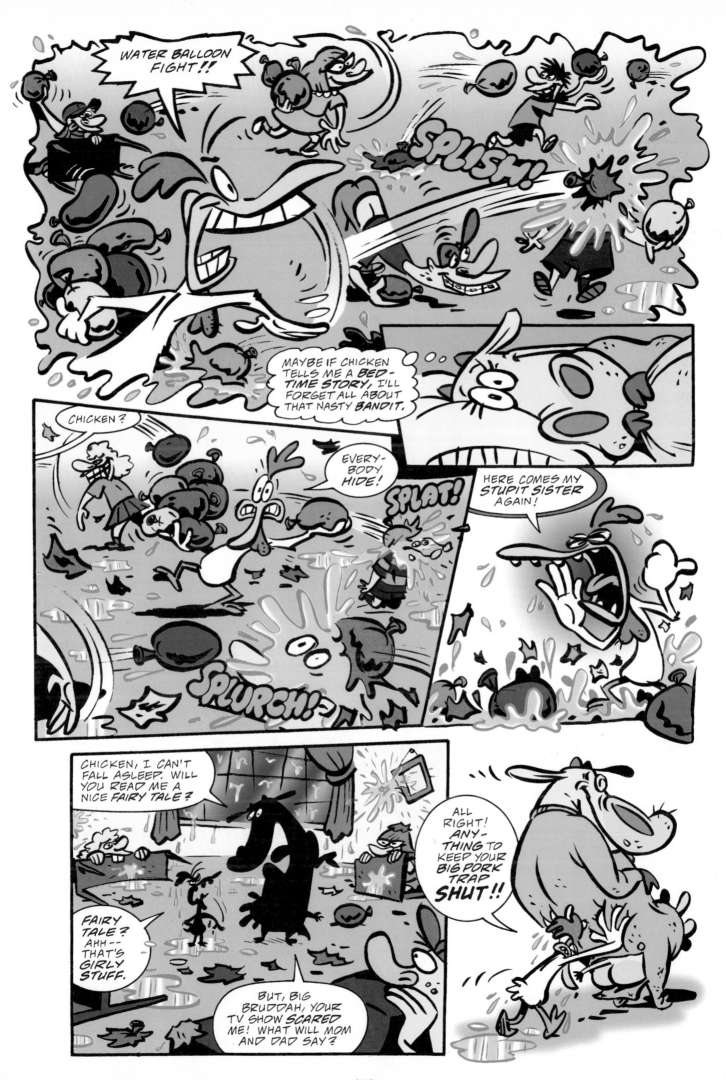

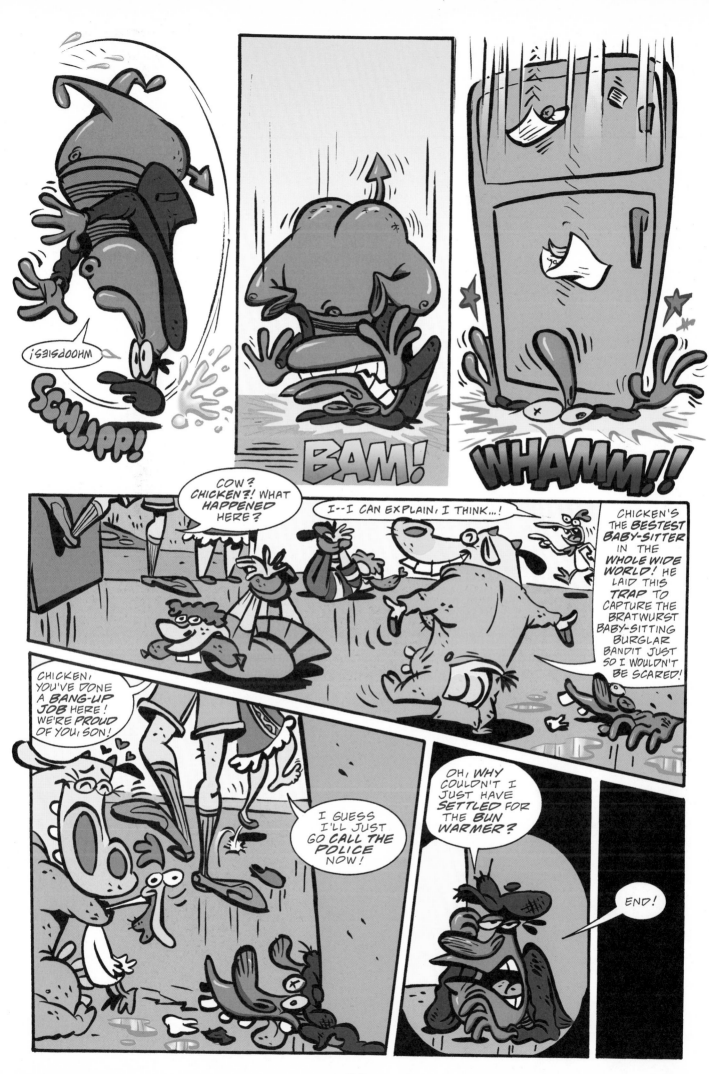

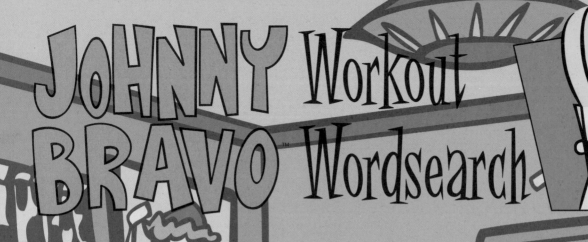

JOHNNY Workout BRAVO™ Wordsearch

P	U	L	L	U	P	S	M
R	U	N	E	X	K	Q	A
E	O	M	E	I	L	U	R
S	R	W	P	C	A	A	A
S	I	S	M	I	W	S	T
U	E	I	V	I	R	H	H
P	W	D	E	O	S	O	O
S	T	E	P	U	P	S	N

Ask Johnny to work out the square root of 144 and he'll run a mile. Ask him to workout at the gym, however, and he'll be there like a shot!

All the words below are to do with keeping in trim. They are hidden in the grid opposite, spelt in every direction including backwards. Can you find them all?

When you have finished, there will be some letters left over. Transfer them, in order, to the boxes below and they will spell out Johnny's very favourite form of fitness training!

Press ups, Step ups, Pull ups, Row, Squash, Pump, Iron, Walk, Run, Skip, Swim, Marathon

IN LIKE FLINTSTONE

GLEN HANSON
story & pencils
KEN LOPEZ
letterer
MIKE DeCARLO
inker
GLEN HANSON
colorist
BRONWYN TAGGART
editor

GOOD MORNING, STONEYPENNY.

AGENT W AND AGENT B! THANK GOODNESS YOU'RE HERE!

COMMANDER SHALE IS WAITING ON THE VIEW SCREEN TO SEE YOU.

85

92

JOHNNY BRAVO™

Wrong Again!

> Hi, guys! Guess what? Johnny's done my homework for me, but I think he's got it a bit wrong.. (of course!) Have a look at his crazy answers and help me by writing the correct ones underneath.....

1) WHAT IS THE CAPITAL OF NORWAY

Johnny's answer – OXO

Your answer _____

2) WHO BUILT ST PAUL'S CATHEDRAL IN LONDON?

Johnny's answer – CHRISTOPHER ROBIN

Your answer _____

3) CORRECT THIS SENTENCE: "IT WAS ME WHAT BROKE THE WINDOW"

Johnny's answer – It wasn't me what broke the window

Your answer _____

4) WRITE A SENTENCE USING THE WORD 'LITRE"

Johnny's answer – Next door's cat had a litre of kittens.

Your answer _____
_____

5) WHAT IS A VANDAL?

Johnny's answer – An open- toed shoe worn by geeks like Dweeb

Your answer_____
_____

6) WHO WAS MACBETH?

Johnny's answer – The horse belonging to that highwayman – guy, Dick Turpin.

Your answer _____
_____
_____

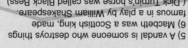

Answers – You should have written:
1) OSLO
2) Christopher Wren
3) It was me who broke the window
4) I bought a litre of milk (or anything similar featuring liquid)
5) A vandal is someone who destroys things
6) Macbeth was a Scottish king, made famous in a play by William Shakespeare. (Dick Turpin's horse was called Black Bess)

JOHNNY BRAVO

Check This Out!

This is where I crash, guys. Take a look at the top picture. Is that one groovy pad or what! Now cast your peepers over the bottom picture. Which Ten Items have been taken from my room?

Answers
The ten items are:
1) stop sign 2) laundry basket 3) guitar & 4) amplifier 5) speaker 6) boxer shorts 7) barbell 8) stripey print 9) bike trophy 10) babe poster

103

JOHNNY BRAVO™ Hot Stuff!

Sunbathing is so cool! (Actually, it's kinda hot - but you know what I mean!) It lets me tune my tan and show my pecks to the chicks! Wanna know where I soak up my rays? Find out by slippin' these places into the grid and then readin' the middle part downwards. Now pass me that bottle of sun-tan oil please, pretty momma ...

		I			L		
		A				A	
				R		C	
		E					
	A				I		
		F					
	I						
G				C			
		A			E		

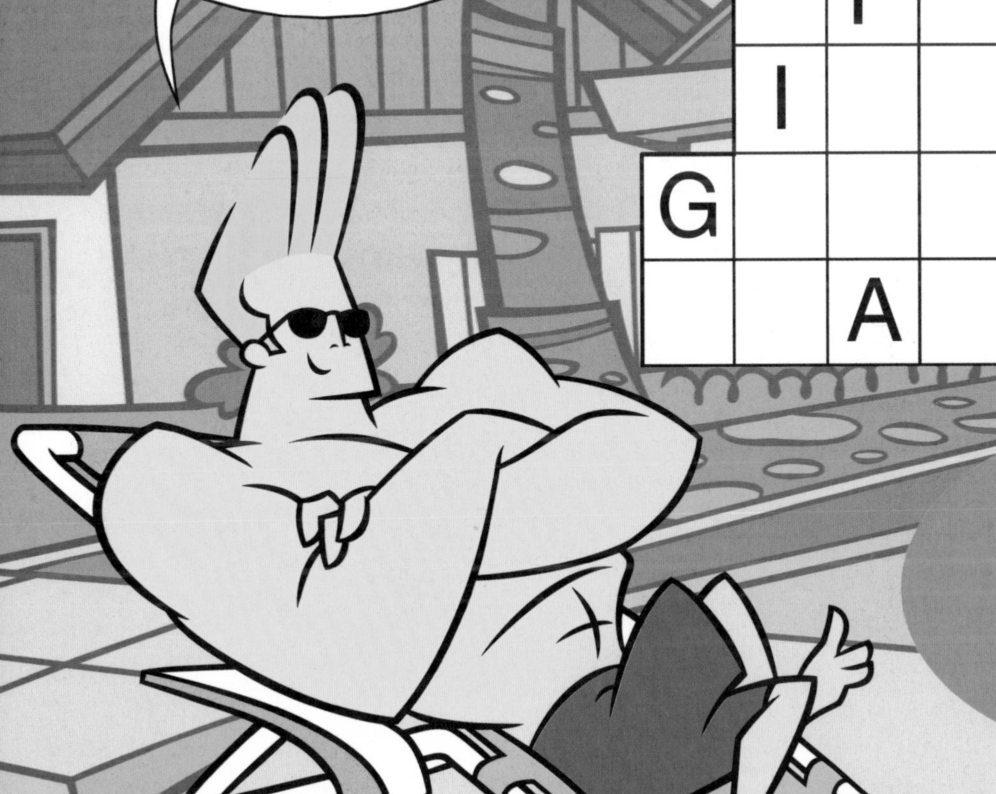

Hawaii
Greece
Egypt
Italy
America
France
Sahara
India
Africa

Answer
Johnny sunbathes in The Garden